How to use this book

Follow the advice, in italics, given for you on each page.
Support the children as they read the text that is shaded in cream.
Praise *the children at every step!*

Detailed guidance is provided in the Read Write Inc. Phonics Handbook

9 reading activities

Children:
Practise reading the speed sounds.
Read the green, red and challenge words for the story.
Listen as you read the introduction.
Discuss the vocabulary check with you.
Read the story.
Re-read the story and discuss the 'questions to talk about'.
Read the story with fluency and expression.
Answer the questions to 'read and answer'.
Practise reading the speed words.

Speed sounds

Vowels *Say the sounds in and out of order.*

a	e	i	o	u	ay	ee	igh	ow
	ea				a͡-e	ea	i͡-e	o͡-e
					a	e	i	oa
					ai	y	y	o
					aigh			

oo	oo	ar	or	air	ir	ou	oy
u͡-e			oor	are	ur	ow	oi
ue			ore		er		
			aw				

Word endings *Make a list of words with these endings.*

<u>t</u>ure	<u>ou</u>s	ab<u>le</u>	<u>t</u>ion
	e<u>ou</u>s	ably	
	ci <u>ou</u>s	ib<u>le</u>	
	ti <u>ou</u>s		

*Each box contains one sound but sometimes more than one grapheme. Focus graphemes are **circled**.*

Green words *Read in syllables.*

(celebrate) cel`e`bra + tion celebration	(relate) re`la + tion relation relations	(congratulate) con`grat`u`la + tion congratulations	(inject) in`jec + tion injection	sta + tion station
(complete) com`ple + tion completion	(prepare) pre`par`a + tion preparation	(digest) in`di`ges + tion indigestion	(solve) sol`u + tion solution	sec + tion section
(explore) ex`plor`a + tion exploration	(invite) in`vit`a + tion invitation	(add) add`i + tion addition	(attend) a`tten + tion attention	trad`i + tion tradition
(conver se) con`vers`a + tion conversation	(decorate) dec`or`a + tion decoration decorations	(operate) op`er`a + tion operation	(exhaust) ex`haus + tion exhaustion	am`bi + tion ambition
				con`di + tion condition
				men + tion mention

Red words

caught   wor se   come   call   was   said   their

great   everyone   should   who   here   watch

Challenge word

honour

A celebration on Planet Zox

Introduction

Imagine going away on a big space journey. How would you feel when you landed? What do you think your family would say? What would you do celebrate your return?

Do you remember Cosmic Clare and Radar Rob who played dare games on Planet Zox? Clare's dad, Cosmic Clive, has returned from a space mission to Planet Pixel. They have a big celebration to welcome him home. But in the middle of his speech he collapses and has to go to hospital.

Will he be alright or has he brought back a deadly disease?

Story written by Gill Munton
Illustrated by Tim Archbold

Vocabulary check

Discuss the meaning (as used in the story) after the children have read each word.

	definition:	sentence/phrase:
completion	end of	It was a big welcome back to Cosmic Clive, on completion of...
exploration	studying, looking at	...his exploration of Planet Pixel.
presentation	giving an award	And now it's time for the presentation!
ambition	wish, dream	It's always been my ambition to be named Zoxonaut of the year.
honour	something to be proud of	It's a great honour.
solution	answer	That's the only solution.
attention	everyone fussing over you	He was enjoying all the attention.

Punctuation to note in this story:
1. Capital letters to start sentences and full stops to end sentences
2. Capital letters for names
3. Exclamation marks to show anger, shock and surprise
4. 'Wait and see' dots...
5. Speech marks

A celebration on Planet Zox

Cosmic Clive (Cosmic Clare's dad)
had just come back
from a trip to Planet Pixel.
Clare and all her relations
went to the space station to meet him.

When they arrived, Clare's dad was climbing
out of the tail section of the spacecraft,
his face pale green with exhaustion.

The King of Zox was speaking to the crowd:

"... so it's a big welcome back to Cosmic Clive
on completion of his exploration of Planet Pixel!
Cosmic Clive, I name you ... Zoxonaut of the Year!"

"And now it's time for the presentation!" he went on. He handed Clare's dad a bunch of green carnations and a gold space watch.

"This calls for a celebration!" said Cosmic Cath (Clare's mum) when they got back to their crater.

The preparations took three light years. First, Clare's mum sent out the invitations. Then she and Clare hung up lots of decorations, and made a banner saying: 'Congratulations to Cosmic Clive – Zoxonaut of the Year!'

On the day of the party, Clare and her family waited for the guests to arrive.

Soon, Radar Roxy (Radar Rob's mum) was deep in conversation with Meteor Meg, and all the little Asteroids were playing space tag with Clare and Rob. Everyone was having a good time.

Then Clare's mum said,
"Clive, it's time for you to make a speech.
After all, it is a family tradition!"

Clare's dad got to his feet.

"It's always been my ambition to be made
Zoxonaut of the Year," he began.
"It's a great honour …"

But then … crash! Cosmic Clive's long green legs
had folded up underneath him!

"It's probably just indigestion," said Clare's mum.
"He should never have had that huge portion of cyber jelly …"

But now pink spots were beginning to appear on Clive's chest.
In addition, he was groaning and wiggling his twenty-six toes.

Plenty of Pixelitis lotion

"His condition's getting worse!"
cried Meteor Meg (who used to be a nurse).
"We must get him into astrohospital!"

In the astrohospital, Clare's mum discussed his condition with the space doctor.

"It's a bad case of Planet Pixelitis," he replied.
"He must have caught it on his trip."

"Will he need an operation?"

"Oh, no. Just an injection – and plenty of Pixelitis lotion on those spots. He'll have to stay in astrohospital for a few weeks."

"But he can't!" cried Clare's mum.

"I hate to mention it, but he's in the middle of a speech!"

"Well, he'll have to finish his speech here, then," said the doctor.
"That's the only solution, I'm afraid."

So Cosmic Clare, Radar Rob and his mum, Meteor Meg
and all the little Asteroids made their way to the space hospital.

And there, opening his get-well cards
and enjoying all the attention,
Cosmic Clive finished his speech –
and another huge portion of cyber jelly!

Questions to talk about

Re-read the page. Read the question to the children. Tell them whether it is a **FIND IT** question or **PROVE IT** question.

FIND IT	PROVE IT
✓ Turn to the page	✓ Turn to the page
✓ Read the question	✓ Read the question
✓ Find the answer	✓ Find your evidence
	✓ Explain why

Page 9:	PROVE IT	Why was Clive's face 'pale green with exhaustion'?
Page 10:	PROVE IT	How do you think Cosmic Clive felt when he was named 'Zoxonaut of the Year!'? What do you think a zoxonaut is?
Page 11:	FIND IT	What did the family do to get ready for the party?
Page 12:	FIND IT	Why did Mum want Clive to make a speech? Do you think he wanted to?
Page 13:	FIND IT	What happened to Clive as he started his speech?
Page 14:	FIND IT	What was the matter with Clive?
Page 15:	PROVE IT	Why did everyone from the party come to the hospital? Do you think Clive would have been well enough to finish his speech?

Questions to read and answer

(Children complete without your help.)

1. Where has Cosmic Clive been on his trip?

2. What does Clare's mum prepare for the party?

3. Why does Clive have to make a speech?

4. What was wrong with Clive?

5. How did Cosmic Clive feel at the end of the story?

Speed words

Children practise reading the words across the rows, down the columns and in and out of order clearly and quickly.

arrive	probably	beginning	underneath	replied
appear	conversation	invitation	injection	addition
attention	decoration	caught	love	wear
talk	watch	mother	could	would

18